the Perfect Pet

story by
Cheyenne Cisco

illustrations by
Bill Mayer

HARCOURT BRACE & COMPANY

Orlando   Atlanta   Austin   Boston   San Francisco   Chicago   Dallas   New York
Toronto   London

Achoo!
We can't get a dog.

Achoo!
We can't get a cat.

Achoo! Achoo!

We can't get a mouse.

Achoo!
We can't get a bird.

Look!

It's the perfect pet!